Math Mammoth
Grade 2 Tests and
Cumulative Reviews

for the complete curriculum
(Light Blue Series)

Includes consumable student copies of:

- Chapter Tests
- End-of-year Test
- Cumulative Reviews

By Maria Miller

Contents

Grade 2, Chapter 1

End-of-Chapter Test

Instructions to the student:

Answer each question in the space provided.

Instructions to the teacher:

My suggestion for grading the chapter 1 test is below. The total is 24 points. Divide the student's score by the total of 24 to get a decimal number, and change that decimal to percent to get the student's percentage score.

Question #	Max. points	Student score
1	8 points	
2	2 points	
3	6 points	

Question #	Max. points	Student score
4	2 points	
5	6 points	
Total	24 points	

Chapter 1 Test   5/5 (A+)

1. Add and subtract.

a.	b.	c.	d.
58 + 2 = 60 ✓	33 + 4 = 37 ✓	50 + 6 = 56 ✓	45 + 40 = 85 ✓
58 − 6 = 52 ✓	94 − 4 = 90 ✓	65 − 30 = 35 ✓	98 − 70 = 28 ✓

2. Color.

 ✓    ✓

a. The fourth flower from the left.   **b.** The sixth flower from the right.

3. Fill in the missing numbers. The four problems form a fact family.

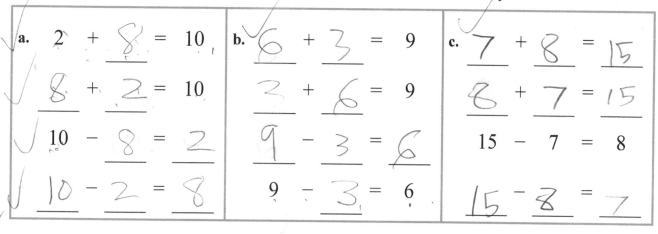

a.
2 + 8 = 10
8 + 2 = 10
10 − 8 = 2
10 − 2 = 8

b.
6 + 3 = 9
3 + 6 = 9
9 − 3 = 6
9 − 3 = 6

c.
7 + 8 = 15
8 + 7 = 15
15 − 7 = 8
15 − 8 = 7

4. You read 23 pages in a story book. Your friend Sally read double that many pages. How many pages did Sally read?

46

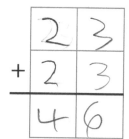

	2	3
+	2	3
	4	6

5. Are these numbers even or odd? Mark an "X".

Number	Even?	Odd?
4	X	
10	X	

Number	Even?	Odd?
9		X
16	X	

Number	Even?	Odd?
11		X
18	X	

Grade 2, Chapter 2

End-of-Chapter Test

Instructions to the student:

Answer each question in the space provided.

Instructions to the teacher:

My suggestion for grading the chapter 2 test is below. The total is 29 points. Divide the student's score by the total of 29 to get a decimal number, and change that decimal to percent to get the student's percentage score.

Question #	Max. points	Student score
1	16 points	
2	4 points	
3	4 points	

Question #	Max. points	Student score
4	5 points	
Total	29 points	

Chapter 2 Test

1. Write the time with hours:minutes, and using "past", "till", "half past" or "o'clock".

a.	b.	c.	d.
2:05	5:45	2:40	6:30
5 past 2	15 till 6	20 till 3	half past 6

e.	f.	g.	h.
3:35	7:25	8:50	4:00
25 till 4	25 past 7	10 till 9	4 o'clock

2. Write the later time.

Time now	3:50	7:25
5 minutes later	3:55	7:30

Time now	9 AM	12 noon
1 hour later	10 am	1 noon

3. Write the time using the **hours:minutes** way.

a. 20 past 4	**b.** 15 past 11	**c.** 15 till 12	**d.** 25 till 7
4:20	11:15	11:45	6:45

4. How many hours pass?

from	5 AM	8 AM	2 AM	10 AM	11 AM
to	12 noon	2 PM	3 PM	10 PM	6 PM
hours	7	7	13	12	7

Grade 2, Chapter 3

End-of-Chapter Test

Instructions to the student:

Answer each question in the space provided.

Instructions to the teacher:

My suggestion for grading the chapter 3 test is below. The total is 31 points. Divide the student's score by the total of 31 to get a decimal number, and change that decimal to percent to get the student's percentage score.

Question #	Max. points	Student score
1	12 points	
2	6 points	
3	3 points	

Question #	Max. points	Student score
4	6 points	
5	4 points	
Total	31 points	

Chapter 3 Test

1. Add and find the missing numbers.

a. $9 + 6 =$ 15	**b.** $8 + 9 =$ 17	**c.** $7 +$ 7 $= 14$
$9 + 4 =$ 13	$7 + 5 =$ 12	$7 +$ 9 $= 16$
d. $9 +$ 3 $= 12$	**e.** $8 + 5 =$ 13	**f.** $6 + 8 =$ 14
$9 +$ 9 $= 18$	$6 + 7 =$ 13	$8 + 7 =$ 15

2. Subtract. For each problem write a corresponding addition fact.

a. $14 - 5 =$ _____	**b.** $11 - 8 =$ _____	**c.** $17 - 8 =$ _____
____ $+$ ____ $=$ ____	____ $+$ ____ $=$ ____	____ $+$ ____ $=$ ____

3. Write $<$, $>$, or $=$.

a. $7 + 9$ ☐ $8 + 8$ **b.** $40 - 5$ ☐ $40 - 8$ **c.** $\frac{1}{2}$ of 20 ☐ $\frac{1}{2}$ of 18

4. Subtract.

a. $11 - 6 =$ _____	**b.** $16 - 8 =$ _____	**c.** $13 - 6 =$ _____
$17 - 9 =$ _____	$14 - 8 =$ _____	$15 - 8 =$ _____

5. Solve.

a. Annie has 7 more teddy bears than Jason. Jason has 9. How many does Annie have?
b. You have saved \$7 to buy a book that costs \$14. Then, Grandma gives you \$5. How much money do you still need?

Grade 2, Chapter 4

End-of-Chapter Test

Instructions to the student:

Answer each question in the space provided.

Instructions to the teacher:

My suggestion for grading the chapter 4 test is below. The total is 21 points. Divide the student's score by the total of 21 to get a decimal number, and change that decimal to percent to get the student's percentage score.

Question #	Max. points	Student score
1	5 points	
2	6 points	
3	4 points	

Question #	Max. points	Student score
4	6 points	
Total	21 points	

Chapter 4 Test

1. Add.

a.	b.	c.	d.	e.
3 9 + 4 6	8 3 1 4 + 2 5	4 6 8 + 3 3	3 8 + 2 3	2 4 7 5 8 +1 5

2. Add.

a. 52 + 7 = _____	**b.** 67 + 6 = _____	**c.** 88 + 5 = _____
18 + 5 = _____	27 + 8 = _____	43 + 8 = _____

3. Add mentally.

a. 2 + 6 + 8 + 7 = _____	**b.** 42 + 2 + 10 + 5 = _____
5 + 7 + 4 + 8 = _____	30 + 30 + 9 + 7 = _____

4. Solve the problems.

a. Mary worked for 28 hours and Jill worked for 13. How many more hours did Mary work than Jill? 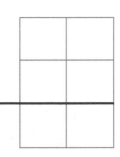	b. Find the total cost if you buy a stuffed animal for $12 and two books for $17 each. 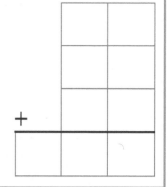

c. Fifteen birds were perching on a tree. Then, nine more birds flew in, and two birds flew away. How many birds are in the tree now?

Grade 2, Chapter 5

End-of-Chapter Test

Instructions to the student:

Answer each question in the space provided.

Instructions to the teacher:

My suggestion for grading the chapter 5 test is below. The total is 22 points. Divide the student's score by the total of 22 to get a decimal number, and change that decimal to percent to get the student's percentage score.

Question #	Max. points	Student score
1	4 points	
2	2 points	
3	2 points	
4	4 points	

Question #	Max. points	Student score
5	4 points	
6	6 points	
Total	22 points	

Chapter 5 Test

1. Join the dots with lines. Use a ruler. Write the name of the shape you get.

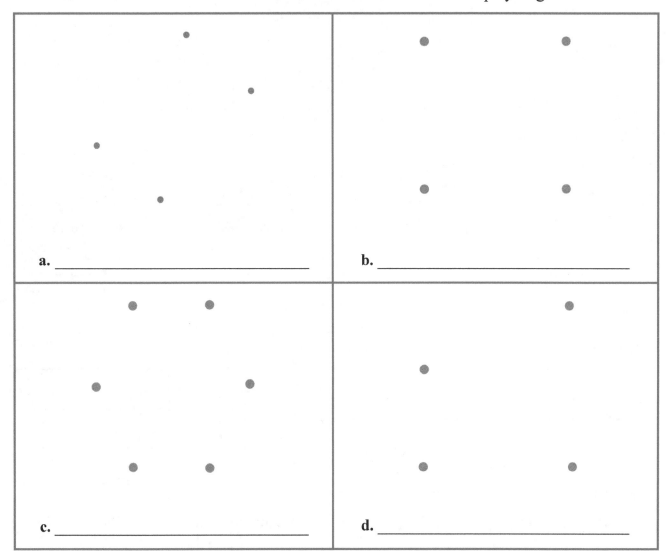

a. _____

b. _____

c. _____

d. _____

2. Draw a rectangle or a square so it encloses the given number of smaller squares.

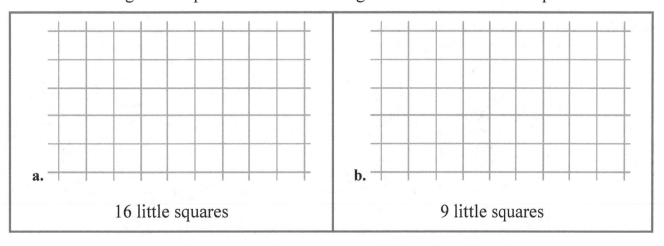

a.

16 little squares

b.

9 little squares

3. Design a pattern with rectangles
   and/or squares.

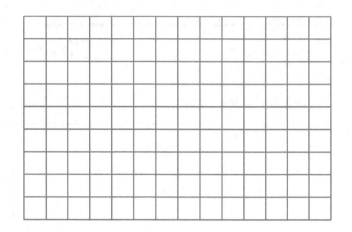

4. Write the fraction.

          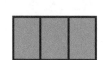

    a. ____   b. ____   c. ____   d. ____

5. Divide these shapes. Then color as you are asked to.

a.	b.	c.	d.
		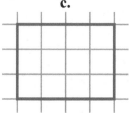	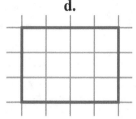
Divide this into thirds. Color $\frac{1}{3}$.	Divide this into halves. Color $\frac{2}{2}$.	Divide this into halves. Color $\frac{1}{2}$.	Divide this into fourths. Color $\frac{3}{4}$.

6. Color. Then compare and write $<$, $>$, or $=$.

a.	b.	c.
$\frac{1}{3}$ $\frac{2}{5}$	$\frac{5}{6}$ $\frac{3}{4}$	$\frac{3}{3}$ $\frac{4}{4}$

Grade 2, Chapter 6

End-of-Chapter Test

Instructions to the student:

Answer each question in the space provided.

Instructions to the teacher:

My suggestion for grading the chapter 6 test is below. The total is 33 points. Divide the student's score by the total of 33 to get a decimal number, and change that decimal to percent to get the student's percentage score.

Question #	Max. points	Student score
1	5 points	.
2	2 points	
3	4 points	
4	4 points	
5	2 points	

Question #	Max. points	Student score
6	4 points	
7	3 points	
8	6 points	
9	3 points	
Total	33 points	

Chapter 6 Test

1. **a.** Count by fives:

475, 480, _____, _____, _____, _____, _____

   b. Count by tens:

376, 386, _____, _____, _____, _____, _____

2. Break these numbers into hundreds, tens, and ones.

a.	b.
235 = _____ + _____ + _____	805 = _____ + _____ + _____

3. These numbers are broken into their hundreds, tens, and ones. Write the numbers.

a. $600 + 80 + 8 =$ _____	b. $80 + 200 + 5 =$ _____
$400 + 60 =$ _____	$100 + 6 =$ _____

4. Write either < or > between the numbers.

a. 159 300	b. 323 230	c. 450 504	d. 482 284

5. Arrange the numbers in order.

a. 689, 869, 986	b. 524, 245, 452
_____ < _____ < _____	_____ < _____ < _____

6. Compare the expressions and write <, >, or = .

   a. $6 + 200 + 50$ ☐ 256 **b.** $800 + 9$ ☐ $90 + 800$

   c. $400 + 60 + 2$ ☐ $40 + 6 + 200$ **d.** $3 + 700$ ☐ $700 + 6$

7. One of the "parts" for the numbers is missing. Find out what number the triangle represents.

a. $300 + \triangle + 7 = 347$	b. $900 + \triangle + 40 = 948$	c. $5 + \triangle + 80 = 585$
$\triangle$ = _____	$\triangle$ = _____	$\triangle$ = _____

8. Add and subtract.

a.	b.	c.
$765 - 200 =$ _____	$802 - 400 =$ _____	$778 - 500 =$ _____
$548 - 300 =$ _____	$980 - 600 =$ _____	$994 - 900 =$ _____

9. Children counted cars that were passing by while waiting for the bus.

   One in the pictograph means 5 cars.

Cars that children counted	
Jayden	🚗 🚗 🚗 🚗 🚗 🚗 🚗
Natalie	🚗 🚗 🚗 🚗 🚗
Caleb	🚗 🚗 🚗 🚗

🚗 = 5 cars

   a. How many cars did Natalie count?

   b. How many did Jayden count?

   c. How many more did Natalie count than Caleb?

Grade 2, Chapter 7

End-of-Chapter Test

Instructions to the student:

Answer each question in the space provided.

Instructions to the teacher:

My suggestion for grading the chapter 7 test is below. The total is 17 points. Divide the student's score by the total of 17 to get a decimal number, and change that decimal to percent to get the student's percentage score.

Question #	Max. points	Student score
1	4 points	
2	4 points	
3	2 points	
4	1 points	

Question #	Max. points	Student score
5	1 points	
6	4 points	
7	1 points	
Total	17 points	

Chapter 7 Test

1. Cross out the sentences that don't make sense.

   a. An 11-year old boy weighs 12 pounds. **b.** An elephant is 3 m tall.

   c. My science book is 25 m wide. **d.** The suitcase weighs 400 kg.

2. Measure these pencils two times, to the nearest half-inch, and to the nearest centimeter.

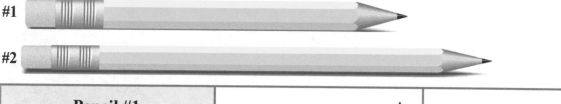

#1

#2

Pencil #1	in.	cm
Pencil #2	in.	cm

3. **a.** Draw a line that is
   4 1/2 inches long.

   b. Draw a line that is
   9 cm long.

4. Arrange these measuring units from the shortest to the longest.

   kilometer   inch   centimeter   foot

5. Andy measured how long a piece of rope is. It was 10 feet long. Then he measured the same rope in meters. Which measurement did Andy get? **10 m   3 m   30 m**

6. Choose a unit to measure these: centimeters (cm), meters (m), or kilometers (km).

Distance	Unit	Distance	Unit
from Florida to California		length of a garden	
around your head		height of a room	

7. The teacher needs to arrange this task beforehand, and check students' results.

   Your teacher gives you an item. Find out how heavy it is. _____

Grade 2, Chapter 8

End-of-Chapter Test

Instructions to the student:

Answer each question in the space provided.

Instructions to the teacher:

My suggestion for grading the chapter 8 test is below. The total is 27 points. Divide the student's score by the total of 27 to get a decimal number, and change that decimal to percent to get the student's percentage score.

Question #	Max. points	Student score
1	4 points	
2	4 points	
3	6 points	

Question #	Max. points	Student score
4	2 points	
5	11 points	
Total	27 points	

Chapter 8 Test

1. Add and subtract.

a. 2 1 9 +4 3 5	b. 5 6 2 +3 7 5	c. 4 9 6 +2 8 6	d. 6 2 −2 7

2. Subtract. Check by adding the result and what was subtracted.

a. 9 6 4 −2 2 7 +_____	b. 7 4 8 −3 7 2 +_____

3. Add and subtract mentally.

a.	b.	c.
80 + 40 = _____	690 + 60 = _____	93 − 52 = _____
280 + 50 = _____	85 − 31 = _____	91 − 89 = _____

4. Find the total bill when Nancy paid for three nights
   in a hotel, at $129 per night.

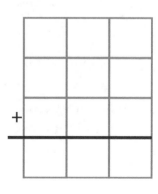

5. Solve the word problems.

a. In a storehouse there were 250 sacks of wheat.
   Then the store owner sold 68 sacks.

   How many sacks are left?

b. A pet store has 52 kittens. Of them, 15 are white
   and 18 are orange. The rest are black.

   How many are black?

c. Jackie bought two 15-lb bags of cat food, and one 50-lb bag of dog food.
   What is the total weight of these bags?

d. One month, a store sold 47 coffee makers
   in January. The next month they sold 19
   fewer coffee makers. How many coffee
   makers did the store sell in February?

   How many did they sell in those two months?

e. Grandpa walked 300 meters on Tuesday.
   The next day he walked 120 meters more
   than on Tuesday. How many meters did
   he walk in those two days all totaled?

Grade 2, Chapter 9

End-of-Chapter Test

Instructions to the student:

Answer each question in the space provided.

Instructions to the teacher:

My suggestion for grading the chapter 9 test is below. The total is 10 points. Divide the student's score by the total of 10 to get a decimal number, and change that decimal to percent to get the student's percentage score.

Question #	Max. points	Student score
1	4 points	
2	2 points	

Question #	Max. points	Student score
4	4 points	
Total	10 points	

Chapter 9 Test

1. How much money? Write the amount.

a. $_____

b. $_____

c. $_____

d. $_____

2. Find the change.

<table>
<tr><td>

a. $1.88

Customer gives $2.00

Change $_____

</td><td>

b. $2.85

Customer gives $5

Change $_____

</td></tr>
</table>

3. Find the total cost.

<table>
<tr><td>

a. Matt bought two sandwiches for $1.56 each and water for $0.78.

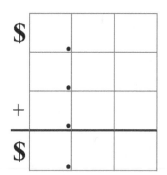

</td><td>

b. Eva bought two sets of water paints for $2.55 each.

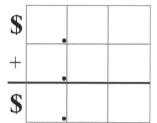

</td></tr>
</table>

Grade 2, Chapter 10

End-of-Chapter Test

Instructions to the student:

Answer each question in the space provided.

Instructions to the teacher:

My suggestion for grading the chapter 10 test is below. The total is 26 points. Divide the student's score by the total of 26 to get a decimal number, and change that decimal to percent to get the student's percentage score.

Question #	Max. points	Student score
1	6 points	
2	2 points	
3	2 points	

Question #	Max. points	Student score
4	4 points	
5	12 points	
Total	26 points	

Chapter 10 Test

1. Draw groups to illustrate the multiplication.

a. $6 \times 1 =$ _____	**b.** $2 \times 7 =$ _____	**c.** $3 \times 3 =$ _____

2. Write each addition as a multiplication.   3. Write each multiplication as an addition.

a. $6 + 6 + 6 + 6 =$ _____ $\times$ _____   **a.** $2 \times 8 =$ _____

b. $50 + 50 + 50 =$ _____ $\times$ _____   **b.** $5 \times 3 =$ _____

4. Draw number-line jumps for these multiplications.

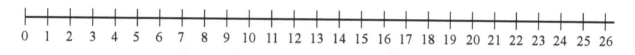

a. $6 \times 3 =$ _____

b. $5 \times 5 =$ _____

5. Multiply.

a. $4 \times 3 =$ _____ $3 \times 10 =$ _____	**b.** $5 \times 0 =$ _____ $2 \times 20 =$ _____	**c.** $1 \times 6 =$ _____ $2 \times 9 =$ _____
d. $4 \times 3 =$ _____ $2 \times 8 =$ _____	**e.** $2 \times 12 =$ _____ $3 \times 5 =$ _____	**f.** $4 \times 10 =$ _____ $1 \times 800 =$ _____

Grade 2 End-of-the Year Test

This test is quite long, so I do not recommend having the student do it in one sitting. Break it into parts and administer them either on consecutive days, or perhaps in the morning/evening/morning. Use your judgment.

This is to be used as a diagnostic test. Thus, you may even skip those areas and concepts that you already know for sure your student has mastered.

The test checks for all major concepts covered in *Math Mammoth Grade 2*. This test is evaluating the student's ability in the following content areas:

- basic addition and subtraction facts within 0-18
- three-digit numbers and place value
- regrouping in addition with two- and three-digit numbers
- regrouping in subtraction with two- and three-digit numbers, excluding regrouping two times
- addition and subtraction
- basic word problems
- measuring and drawing with a ruler, to the nearest centimeter
- names and usage of units for measuring length and weight
- names of basic shapes
- the concept of a fraction
- reading the clock to the nearest five minutes
- counting coins and banknotes
- the concept of multiplication

Note: Problems #1 and #2 are done <u>orally and timed</u>. Let the student see the problems. Read each problem aloud, and wait a maximum of 5 seconds for an answer. Mark the problem as right or wrong according to the student's (oral) answer. Mark it wrong if there is no answer. Then you can move on to the next problem.

You do not have to mention to the student that the problems are timed or that he/she will have 5 seconds per answer, because the idea here is not to create extra pressure by the fact it is timed, but simply to check if the student has the facts memorized (quick recall). You can say for example (vary as needed):

"I will ask you some addition and subtraction questions. Try to answer them as quickly as possible. In each question, I will only wait a little bit for you to answer, and if you do not say anything, I will move on to the next problem. So just try your best to answer the questions as quickly as you can."

In order to continue with *Math Mammoth Grade 3*, I recommend that the student score at least 80% on this test, and that the teacher or parent revise with him any content areas in which he is weak. Students scoring between 70% and 80% may also continue with grade 3, depending on the types of errors (careless errors or not remembering something, versus lack of understanding). The most important areas to master are topics related to addition and subtraction, word problems, and place value. Again, use your judgment.

My suggestion for grading is below. The total is 134 points. A score of 107 points is 80%.

Question	Max. points	Student score
Basic Addition and Subtraction Facts		
1	16 points	
2	16 points	
3	6 points	
	subtotal	/ 38
Mental Addition and Subtraction with Two-Digit Numbers and Word Problems		
4	1 point	
5	2 points	
6	3 points	
7	1 point	
8	3 points	
9	3 points	
10	6 points	
	subtotal	/ 19
Three-Digit Numbers		
11	2 points	
12	2 points	
13	2 points	
14	6 points	
15	4 points	
	subtotal	/ 16
Regrouping in Addition and Subtraction, Including Word Problems		
16	3 points	
17	4 points	
18	2 points	
19	2 points	
20	2 points	
21	3 points	
	subtotal	/ 16

Question	Max. points	Student score
Clock		
22	6 points	
23	5 points	
	subtotal	/ 11
Money		
24	2 points	
25	2 points	
26	2 points	
	subtotal	/ 6
Geometry and Measuring		
27	2 points	
28	4 points	
29	1 point	
30	4 points	
	subtotal	/ 11
Fractions		
31	4 points	
32	6 points	
	subtotal	/ 10
Concept of Multiplication		
33	2 points	
34	2 points	
35	3 points	
	subtotal	/ 7
	TOTAL	/ 134

End of Year Test - Grade 2

Basic Addition and Subtraction Facts

In problems 1 and 2, your teacher will read you the addition and subtraction questions. Try to answer them as quickly as possible. In each question, he/she will only wait a little while for you to answer, and if you don't say anything, your teacher will move on to the next problem. So just try your best to answer the questions as quickly as you can.

1. Add.

a.	b.	c.	d.
$6 + 7 = $ _____	$7 + 4 = $ _____	$8 + 8 = $ _____	$9 + 5 = $ _____
$9 + 9 = $ _____	$5 + 8 = $ _____	$6 + 6 = $ _____	$7 + 7 = $ _____
$5 + 6 = $ _____	$3 + 9 = $ _____	$2 + 9 = $ _____	$8 + 6 = $ _____
$8 + 7 = $ _____	$5 + 7 = $ _____	$4 + 8 = $ _____	$8 + 9 = $ _____

2. Subtract.

a.	b.	c.	d.
$12 - 3 = $ _____	$11 - 3 = $ _____	$14 - 5 = $ _____	$13 - 4 = $ _____
$15 - 7 = $ _____	$12 - 8 = $ _____	$12 - 4 = $ _____	$15 - 6 = $ _____
$13 - 6 = $ _____	$14 - 6 = $ _____	$18 - 9 = $ _____	$12 - 6 = $ _____
$11 - 7 = $ _____	$16 - 8 = $ _____	$16 - 7 = $ _____	$14 - 7 = $ _____

3. Fill in the missing numbers. The four problems form a fact family.

a. $2 + \Box = 11$ $\Box + 2 = 11$ $11 - 2 = \Box$ $11 - \Box = 2$	b. ___ + ___ = 17 ___ + ___ = 17 $17 - 8 = $ ___ $17 - $ ___ $ = $ ___	c. ___ + ___ = ___ ___ + ___ = ___ $12 - $ ___ $ = 5$ ___ − ___ = ___

4. What is double 35?

5. Mary picked 5 apples and Bill picked 9. The children shared all of their apples evenly. How many did each child get?

6. List here the even numbers from 10 to 20.

7. Find the difference of 75 and 90.

8. Ed had saved $16. Then grandma gave him $10. Now how much more does he need in order to buy a toolset for $32?

9. Find the missing numbers.

  a. $82 + \underline{\hspace{1cm}} = 90$ **b.** $13 + \underline{\hspace{1cm}} = 21$ **c.** $90 - \underline{\hspace{1cm}} = 83$

10. Calculate mentally.

a. $59 + 8 = \underline{\hspace{1.5cm}}$	**b.** $52 + 40 = \underline{\hspace{1.5cm}}$	**c.** $76 - 50 = \underline{\hspace{1.5cm}}$
$62 + 8 = \underline{\hspace{1.5cm}}$	$45 + 9 = \underline{\hspace{1.5cm}}$	$54 - 23 = \underline{\hspace{1.5cm}}$

Three-Digit Numbers

11. Write with numbers.

  a. 6 tens 2 hundreds 7 ones = $\underline{\hspace{2cm}}$ **b.** 8 ones 9 hundreds = $\underline{\hspace{2cm}}$

12. Skip-count by tens.

    568, 578, $\underline{\hspace{2cm}}$, $\underline{\hspace{2cm}}$, $\underline{\hspace{2cm}}$, $\underline{\hspace{2cm}}$, $\underline{\hspace{2cm}}$

13. Write the numbers in order from the smallest to the greatest.

a. 417, 714, 447	**b.** 89, 998, 809

14. Calculate mentally.

a. 560 + 40 = _____	**b.** 520 − 20 = _____	**c.** 362 − 30 = _____
560 + 400 = _____	520 − 200 = _____	362 − 300 = _____

15. Compare the expressions and write $<$, $>$, or $=$.

a. $100 - 5 - 3 \;\boxed{}\; 98 - 6$ b. $40 + 8 + 200 \;\boxed{}\; 20 + 800 + 4$

c. $50 + 120 \;\boxed{}\; 125$ d. $\frac{1}{2}$ of $800 \;\boxed{}\; 399 + 5$

Regrouping in Addition and Subtraction, including Word Problems

16. Add.

a.
```
   3 5
   3 6
 + 1 2
 ──────
```

b.
```
   2 2 4
 + 4 5 8
 ────────
```

c.
```
   4 3 8
     1 7
 + 2 9 3
 ────────
```

17. Subtract. Check by adding the result and what was subtracted.

| a. ```
   6 1
 − 3 7
 ──────
``` + _____ | b. ```
   9 7 0
 − 2 4 8
 ────────
``` + _____ |
| --- | --- |

18. Jennifer bought two vacuum cleaners for $152 each.
What was the total cost?

19. A box contains 450 disks in all. Of them,
126 are music CDs and the rest are DVDs.
How many DVDs are in the box?

20. The distance from Mark's home to
his grandma's house is 218 miles.
How many miles long is a round trip?

21. Every day Janet jogs around a rectangular-
shaped jogging track. One side is 150 yards
and another side is 300 yards.

   a. Mark the distances in the picture.

   b. Calculate what distance Janet goes
   when she jogs around it once.

Clock

22. Write the time with *hours:minutes*, and using "past" or "till".

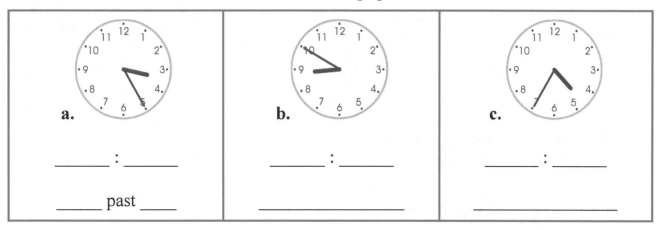

a. _____ : _____

_____ past ____

b. _____ : _____

_____

c. _____ : _____

_____

23. How much time passes? Fill in the table.

from	3:00	2:00	1 AM	11 AM	8 PM
to	3:05	2:30	8 AM	1 PM	midnight
amount of time					

Money

24. How much money? Write the amount.

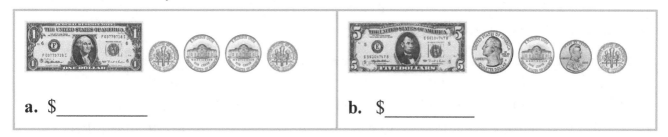

a. $_____

b. $_____

25. Find the change, if you buy a meal for $3.35
    and you pay with $4.

26. Bill bought an eraser that cost 85¢. He paid with $1.
    What was his change?

27. Identify the shapes.

    Shape A: _____

    Shape B: _____

28. **a.** Join the dots in order (A-B-C-D)
    with straight lines. Use a ruler.

    b. What shape is formed?

    _____

    c. Measure the sides of the shape to the nearest half-inch.

    Side AB: about _____   Side BC: about _____

    Side CD: about _____   Side DA: about _____

29. Measure this line to the nearest centimeter.

    ▬▬▬▬▬▬▬▬▬▬▬▬▬▬   about _____ cm

30. Which measuring unit or units could you use to find these amounts?
    Centimeter (cm), inch (in), meter (m), foot (ft), mile (mi), or kilometer (km)?
    Sometimes two different units are possible. If so, write both.

Distance	Unit(s)
how long my pencil is	
the distance from London to New York	
the height of a wall	
the distance it is to the neighbor's house	

Fractions

31. Divide these shapes. Then color as you are asked to.

a.

Divide this into

thirds. Color $\frac{2}{3}$.

b.

Divide this into

halves. Color $\frac{1}{2}$.

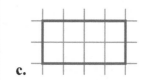

c.

Divide this into

halves. Color $\frac{2}{2}$.

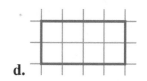

d.

Divide this into

fourths. Color $\frac{3}{4}$.

32. Color. Then compare and write $<$, $>$, or $=$ between the fractions.

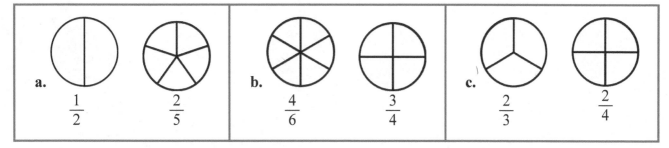

a. $\frac{1}{2}$ $\frac{2}{5}$

b. $\frac{4}{6}$ $\frac{3}{4}$

c. $\frac{2}{3}$ $\frac{2}{4}$

Concept of Multiplication

33. Write a multiplication sentence for each picture.

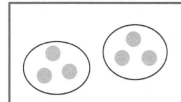

a. _____ × _____ = _____

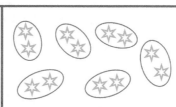

b. _____ × _____ = _____

34. Write a <u>multiplication</u> for each addition, and solve.

a. $5 + 5 + 5$	b. $4 + 4 + 4 + 4 + 4$
_____ × _____ = _____	_____ × _____ = _____

35. Solve.

a. $2 \times 5 =$ _____	b. $3 \times 3 =$ _____	c. $3 \times 10 =$ _____

Using the Cumulative Reviews

The cumulative reviews practice topics in various chapters of the Math Mammoth complete curriculum, up to the chapter named in the review. For example, a cumulative review for chapters 1-6 may include problems matching chapters 1, 2, 3, 4, 5, and 6. The cumulative review lesson for chapters 1-6 can be used any time after the student has studied the curriculum through chapter 6.

These lessons provide additional practice and review. The teacher should decide when and if they are used. The student doesn't have to complete all the cumulative reviews. I recommend using at least three of these reviews during the school year. The teacher can also use the reviews as diagnostic tests to find out what topics the student has trouble with.

Math Mammoth complete curriculum also includes an easy worksheet maker, which is the perfect tool to make more problems for children who need more practice. The worksheet maker covers most topics in the curriculum, excluding word problems. Most people find it to be a very helpful addition to the curriculum.

The download version of the curriculum comes with the worksheet maker, and you can also access the worksheet maker online at

https://www.mathmammoth.com/private/Make_extra_worksheets_grade2.htm

Cumulative Review, Grade 2, Chapters 1 - 2

1. Solve the problems. Fill in the doubles chart. *It has a pattern!* Find it!

   a. It will take Alex 16 hours to clean the park.
      He did half of that yesterday. How many
      hours will he still have to work?

   b. What is double 12?

   c. Ava and Emma divided evenly $30. Then Emma
      bought a gift for $6. How much money does
      Emma have now?

   d. Eddie has saved $20. That is just half of what he needs
      to buy a train set. How much does the train set cost?

$10 + 10 =$ _____

$15 + 15 =$ _____

$20 + 20 =$ _____

$25 + 25 =$ _____

$30 + 30 =$ _____

$35 + 35 =$ _____

$40 + 40 =$ _____

2. Add and subtract whole tens.

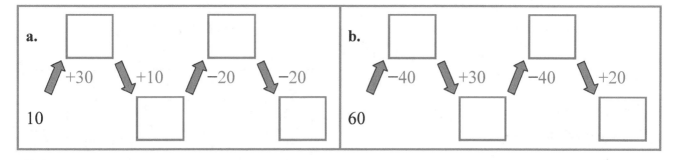

3. Write the time using *hours:minutes*.

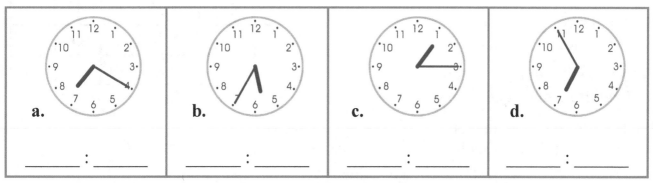

4. **a.** Anne began watching a film about sea animals at 20 till 4. She stopped watching it at 15 past 4. Write those two times in the *hours:minutes* way.

_____ : _____ and _____ : _____

   b. Jim began walking his dog at 11 AM and stopped at noon.
How long did he walk his dog?

   c. Bill's rooster crowed for half an hour, starting at 5 AM.
At what time did it stop?

5. Fill in the missing numbers. The four problems form a fact family.

a. $3 + \boxed{} = 9$

$\boxed{} + 3 = 9$

$9 - 3 = \boxed{}$

$9 - \boxed{} = 3$

b. _____ + _____ = 10

_____ + _____ = 10

$10 - 4 = \boxed{}$

$10 - \boxed{} = 4$

c. _____ + _____ = _____

_____ + _____ = _____

$8 -$ _____ $= 3$

_____ $-$ _____ $=$ _____

6. Find the letters, and find out what Bob got for his birthday.

The second row from the top, the second letter from the left. _____

The fourth row from the top, the fifth letter from the left. _____

The first row from the top, the fifth letter from the right. _____

The fifth row from the bottom, the second letter from the right. _____

The 1st row from the bottom, the 1st letter from the left. _____

The sixth row from the top, the third letter from the right. _____

The 3rd row from the top, the 2nd letter from the left. _____

E	S	H	A	B	G	P
B	A	E	N	I	V	S
W	E	K	P	T	O	F
J	D	A	U	-	W	M
Y	K	Z	N	Y	I	C
U	D	T	S	S	Q	R
R	T	H	A	V	E	L

Cumulative Review, Grade 2, Chapters 1 - 3

1. Add and find the missing addends.

a.	b.	c.	d.
$6 + 7 =$ _____	$9 + 7 =$ _____	$5 +$ _____ $= 14$	$8 +$ _____ $= 15$
$8 + 9 =$ _____	$5 + 8 =$ _____	$8 +$ _____ $= 16$	$7 +$ _____ $= 14$

2. How many hours is it?

from	9 AM	6 AM	11 AM	12 AM	10 AM
to	1 PM	8 PM	4 PM	12 PM	2 PM
hours					

3. **a.** How many Tuesdays are there in January?
(See the calendar on the right.)

b. Jane visits her parents every third Sunday of the month. What day will she visit them in January?

January

Su	Mo	Tu	We	Th	Fr	Sa
		1	2	3	4	5
6	7	8	9	10	11	12
13	14	15	16	17	18	19
20	21	22	23	24	25	26
27	28	29	30	31		

4. Solve.

a. Joyce practices playing the piano for 2 hours.
She stopped practicing at 2 PM. When did she *start* practicing?

b. Grandma sleeps 1/4 of the day's hours. (One day has 24 hours.)
How many hours does Grandma sleep each day?

5. Add and subtract whole tens.

a. $77 + 20 =$ _____	**b.** $18 + 50 =$ _____	**c.** $54 + 40 =$ _____
$64 - 30 =$ _____	$43 - 20 =$ _____	$98 - 60 =$ _____

6. Add more. Find the difference.

a. $18 + \rule{1.5cm}{0.15mm} = 22$	b. $75 + \rule{1.5cm}{0.15mm} = 80$	c. $56 + \rule{1.5cm}{0.15mm} = 59$
d. The difference of 8 and 12 is \rule{1.5cm}{0.15mm}.	e. The difference of 43 and 49 is \rule{1.5cm}{0.15mm}.	f. The difference of 21 and 30 is \rule{1.5cm}{0.15mm}.

7. Subtract. Think about the difference.

a. $85 - 80 = \rule{1.5cm}{0.15mm}$ $46 - 42 = \rule{1.5cm}{0.15mm}$	b. $76 - 71 = \rule{1.5cm}{0.15mm}$ $99 - 89 = \rule{1.5cm}{0.15mm}$	c. $20 - 17 = \rule{1.5cm}{0.15mm}$ $70 - 67 = \rule{1.5cm}{0.15mm}$

8. For each addition, write a matching subtraction (using the same numbers).

a. $8 + \square = 14$ $\rule{1cm}{0.15mm} - \rule{1cm}{0.15mm} = \square$	b. $5 + \square = 14$ $\rule{1cm}{0.15mm} - \rule{1cm}{0.15mm} = \square$	c. $6 + \square = 12$ $\rule{1cm}{0.15mm} - \rule{1cm}{0.15mm} = \square$

9. Subtract.

a.	b.	c.	d.
$12 - 7 = \rule{1cm}{0.15mm}$	$14 - 8 = \rule{1cm}{0.15mm}$	$11 - 6 = \rule{1cm}{0.15mm}$	$15 - 7 = \rule{1cm}{0.15mm}$
$17 - 9 = \rule{1cm}{0.15mm}$	$12 - 8 = \rule{1cm}{0.15mm}$	$13 - 8 = \rule{1cm}{0.15mm}$	$14 - 9 = \rule{1cm}{0.15mm}$
$11 - 8 = \rule{1cm}{0.15mm}$	$13 - 7 = \rule{1cm}{0.15mm}$	$16 - 9 = \rule{1cm}{0.15mm}$	$15 - 9 = \rule{1cm}{0.15mm}$

10. Detective Cole was a math sleuth. He was out to get the fact family. He had found number 13, but two numbers were missing. Help him find the fact family!

He found a clue under the couch: "Look in the cookie jar!" In the cookie jar there were half a dozen cookies left. Cole said, "That's one of my missing numbers!"

Can you figure out the other missing number now? Then, write the fact family.

$\rule{1cm}{0.15mm} + \rule{1cm}{0.15mm} = \rule{1.5cm}{0.15mm}$ $\rule{1.5cm}{0.15mm} - \rule{1cm}{0.15mm} = \rule{1cm}{0.15mm}$

$\rule{1cm}{0.15mm} + \rule{1cm}{0.15mm} = \rule{1.5cm}{0.15mm}$ $\rule{1.5cm}{0.15mm} - \rule{1cm}{0.15mm} = \rule{1cm}{0.15mm}$

The case is solved!

Cumulative Review, Grade 2, Chapters 1 - 4

1. Solve the problems.

a. One-half of the boys in the class are studying math. The other seven boys are reading. How many boys are in the class?
b. Mark has \$8. Andy has double that much money. How much money does Andy have? How much money do the two boys have together?

2. Add mentally.

a. $28 + 4 =$ _____ $28 + 40 =$ _____	**b.** $39 + 9 =$ _____ $30 + 29 =$ _____	**c.** $44 + 5 + 4 =$ _____ $7 + 8 + 9 + 4 =$ _____

3. A few years ago a small camera cost \$67.
   Now it has doubled in price.
   How much does it cost now?

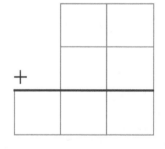

4. Write the time using "past", "till", "half past", or "o'clock".

a. 7:25 _____	**b.** 5:10 _____
c. 5:50 _____	**d.** 12:40 _____
e. 12:30 _____	**f.** 11:00 _____

5. Write the numbers so that ones and tens are in their own columns. Add.

   a. 44 + 37   **b.** 9 + 26   **c.** 26 + 8 + 47   **d.** 25 + 57 + 38

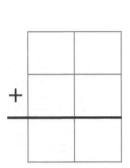 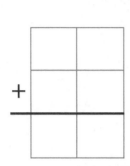 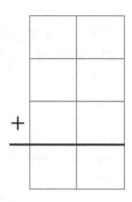 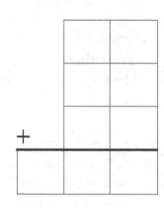

6. Chris made six cards for his party. He put the cards at the plate of each guest.
   It took Chris 10 minutes to make one card.
   a. How long did it take Chris to make all 6 cards?

   b. If he started making the cards at noon, at what time did he finish his project?

7. Fill in the missing numbers.

a. 24 + 8 = ⬭	**b.** 16 − 7 = ⬭	**c.** 17 − 9 = ⬭
d. ⬭ − 6 = 5	**e.** ⬭ − 20 = 7	**f.** ⬭ − 5 = 31

8. You bought three stools for $18
   each and some towels for $25.
   Find the total cost.

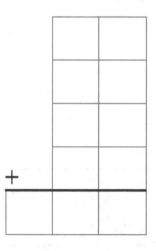

Cumulative Review, Grade 2, Chapters 1 - 5

1. Write two additions and two subtractions for each picture. The box with a "T" is a ten.

a. ☐T/T and ☐T T/T T

_____ + _____ = _____

_____ + _____ = _____

_____ − _____ = _____

_____ − _____ = _____

b. ☐T T ●●●● and ●● ●●●● ●●

_____ + _____ = _____

_____ + _____ = _____

_____ − _____ = _____

_____ − _____ = _____

2. Add.

a. 29 + 90   **b.** 93 + 46   **c.** 24 + 35 + 48   **d.** 22 + 47 + 9

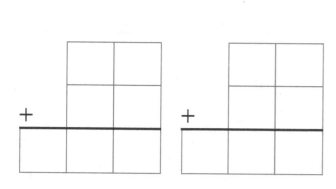

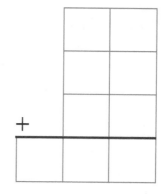

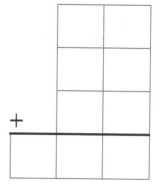

3. Solve.

a. Choose the letters from the given word to make a new word.

M A M M A L

____ ____ ____ ____ ____
6th   6th   5th   3rd   2nd

b. Put the letters in the given order to make a new word.

L   O   I   D   R   N   A
7th   1st   4th   3rd   2nd   5th   6th

O̲ ____ ____ ____ ____ ____ ____

63

4. Write the time that the clock shows, and the time 5 minutes later.

	a. ____ : _____	b. ____ : _____	c. ____ : _____	d. ____ : _____
5 min. later →	____ : _____	____ : _____	____ : _____	____ : _____

5. A flower vase has 15 flowers. Some are red, some are blue, and some are yellow. Four of the flowers are red and five are yellow. How many are blue?

6. Write $<$, $>$, or $=$. You can often compare without calculating!

   a. $8 + 8$ ☐ $9 + 8$ **b.** $30 - 8$ ☐ $30 - 9$ **c.** $\frac{1}{2}$ of 16 ☐ 16

   d. $35 + 7$ ☐ $35 + 8$ **e.** $40 - 6$ ☐ $40 - 9$ **f.** $14 - 7$ ☐ $16 - 8$

7. Add by adding tens and ones separately.

a. $36 + 22$	**b.** $72 + 18$
$30 + 20 + 6 + 2$	$70 + 10 + 2 + 8$
_____ + _____ = _____	_____ + _____ = _____
c. $54 + 37$	**d.** $24 + 55$
_____ + _____ = _____	_____ + _____ = _____

8. Count by 10s and 50s, and fill in the grids.

a.	464	474							

b.	400	450							

Cumulative Review, Grade 2, Chapters 1 - 6

1. Write what place the teddy bear has using ordinal numbers.

   a. The _____ place from the left.

   b. The _____ place from the right.

   c. The _____ place from the left.

   d. The _____ place from the right.

2. Jack is on the track team. He spends a half-hour for warm-up
   exercises, an hour running, and thirty minutes jumping hurdles.
   How much time does he spend practicing?

3. One T-shirt costs $12 and another cost $5 more than that.
   If you buy both, what is the total cost?

4. Add.

a.	b.	c.	d.	e.
3 7	2 9	5 4	3 6	2 8
1 8	8 0	1 3	9	1 8
+ 4 3	+ 3 6	+ 7 6	+ 4 3	+ 3 6

5. Complete the **next whole ten**.

a.	b.	c.
66 + ____ = 70	31 + 3 + _____ = 40	47 + _____ + 1 = 50
92 + ____ = _____	63 + 2 + _____ = 70	32 + _____ + 2 = 40

6. Write the time with *hours:minutes*, and using "past" or "till."

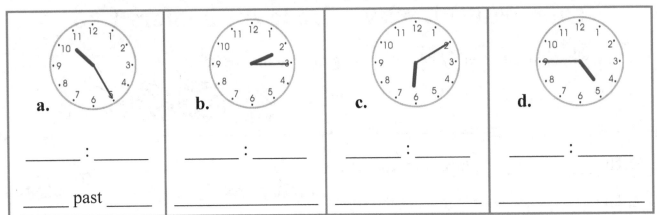

a. _____ : _____

_____ past _____

b. _____ : _____

_____

c. _____ : _____

_____

d. _____ : _____

_____

7. Draw here six dots randomly
   and join them like a dot-to-dot.
   Use a ruler. What shape do
   you get?
   (Hint: It will not be a straight line.)

8. Color <u>one whole pie</u>.
   Write <u>one</u> as a fraction,
   in many different ways.

a. $1 =$ _____   **b.** $1 =$ _____   **c.** $1 =$ _____

9. Divide these shapes. Then color as you are asked to.

a.	**b.**	**c.**	**d.**
		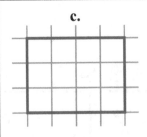	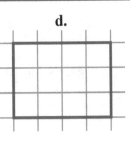
Divide this into halves. Color $\frac{1}{2}$.	Divide this into fourths. Color $\frac{3}{4}$.	Divide this into thirds. Color $\frac{1}{3}$.	Divide this into fourths. Color $\frac{1}{4}$.

Cumulative Review, Grade 2, Chapters 1 - 7

1. Solve.

> **a.** Diane needs 8 apples to make one pie, and she wants to
> make two pies for a bake sale. Diane already has 10 apples.
> How many more apples does Diane need to buy?

> **b.** Joe and Ben are building go-carts. They sold one for $18.
> How much would two go-carts cost?

> **c.** Raylene has four cats. One of them had kittens. Now she has double
> as many cats as before. How many cats does Raylene have now?
>
> How many of them are kittens?

2. Draw the hands on the clock faces to show the given time.

      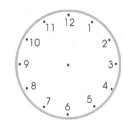

    a. 1:25   **b.** 3:15   **c.** 15 till 3

3. Find the pattern and continue it.

a.
$577 - 10 = \underline{\hspace{2cm}}$

$577 - 20 = \underline{\hspace{2cm}}$

$577 - 30 = \underline{\hspace{2cm}}$

$577 - \underline{\hspace{1cm}} = \underline{\hspace{1.5cm}}$

$\underline{\hspace{1.5cm}} - \underline{\hspace{1cm}} = \underline{\hspace{1.5cm}}$

$\underline{\hspace{1.5cm}} - \underline{\hspace{1cm}} = \underline{\hspace{1.5cm}}$

b.
$926 - 0 = \underline{\hspace{2cm}}$

$926 - 100 = \underline{\hspace{2cm}}$

$926 - 200 = \underline{\hspace{2cm}}$

$\underline{\hspace{1.5cm}} - \underline{\hspace{1.5cm}} = \underline{\hspace{1.5cm}}$

$\underline{\hspace{1.5cm}} - \underline{\hspace{1.5cm}} = \underline{\hspace{1.5cm}}$

$\underline{\hspace{1.5cm}} - \underline{\hspace{1.5cm}} = \underline{\hspace{1.5cm}}$

4. Solve.

a. 9 + 8 = _____	**b.** 8 + 8 = _____	**c.** 5 + 8 = _____
5 + 6 = _____	6 + 6 = _____	4 + 7 = _____
7 + 7 = _____	9 + 7 = _____	6 + 8 = _____

5. Barbara drew some shapes in her notebook.
   She needs you to help her label them.

  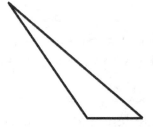

a._____   b. _____   c. _____

6. Draw in the grid a rectangle that is
   6 units wide and 3 units long.

   How many squares are inside it? _____ squares

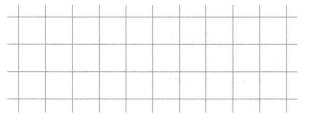

7. Fill in the missing numbers and words in the charts below.

Ordinal Number	Name
	first
2nd	
	fourth
	seventh

Ordinal Number	Name
8th	
	ninth
10th	
	thirteenth

Cumulative Review, Grade 2, Chapters 1 - 8

1. Cross out and subtract. Subtract also in columns!

a. $40 - 29 =$ _____

b. $50 - 28 =$ _____

c. $62 - 25$

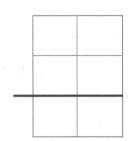

d. $83 - 46$

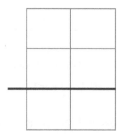

2. Add.

a. $6 + 3 =$ _____	**b.** $7 + 5 =$ _____	**c.** $8 + 6 =$ _____	**d.** $9 + 9 =$ _____
$6 + 10 =$ _____	$7 + 8 =$ _____	$8 + 7 =$ _____	$9 + 4 =$ _____

3. Find these differences. Think of adding more.

a. $17 - 11 =$ _____	**b.** $43 - 37 =$ _____	**c.** $66 - 59 =$ _____
Think: $11 +$ ____ $= 17$	Think: $37 +$ ____ $= 43$	Think: $59 +$ ____ $= 66$
d. $35 - 28 =$ _____	**e.** $80 - 77 =$ _____	**f.** $100 - 94 =$ _____

4. Find what was subtracted.

$-\ \boxed{}\quad -\ \boxed{}\quad -\ \boxed{}\quad -\ \boxed{}\quad -\ \boxed{}\quad -\ \boxed{}\quad -\ \boxed{}$

79 75 71 68 65 59 57 52

5. Write the times using hours : minutes.

a. 15 past 6	**b.** 20 till 3	**c.** 5 past 10	**d.** half past 3
_____ : _____	_____ : _____	_____ : _____	_____ : _____
e. 15 till 8	**f.** 20 till 12	**g.** 5 till 1	**h.** 25 past 1
_____ : _____	_____ : _____	_____ : _____	_____ : _____

6. Dan weighs 138 pounds. His sister weighs twenty pounds less than he does.

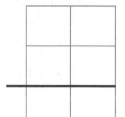

   a. How much does Dan's sister weigh?

   b. How much do they weigh together?

7. **a.** Draw a rectangle. Use a ruler to make it as neat as you can!

   b. Draw a line through the rectangle from one corner to the opposite corner.

   c. What shapes are formed now?

8. **a.** In each picture, color TWO slices of the whole pie, and write the fraction.

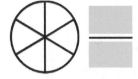 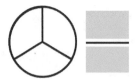 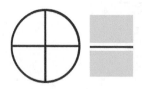 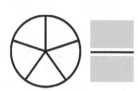

   b. Now, find the largest fraction (the one that has most to eat).

9. Compare, and write < or > .

   a. 106 ☐ 120   **b.** 141 ☐ 114   **c.** 700 + 80 + 9 ☐ 90 + 8 + 700

Cumulative Review, Grade 2, Chapters 1 - 9

1. Color the part indicated.

a. $\frac{1}{2}$ **b.** $\frac{1}{4}$ **c.** $\frac{3}{4}$ **d.** $\frac{2}{4}$ **e.** $\frac{4}{4}$ **f.** $\frac{2}{2}$

2. How many hours pass?

a. From 3:00 to 8:00 _____ hours	**d.** From noon till 4 PM _____ hours
b. From 6 AM to 1 PM _____ hours	**e.** From 7 PM to 11 PM _____ hours
c. From 7 PM to midnight _____ hours	**f.** From 10 AM to 2 PM _____ hours

3. Add and subtract.

a. $7 + 8 =$ _____	**b.** $8 +$ _____ $= 13$	**c.** $14 -$ _____ $= 7$
$4 + 9 =$ _____	$8 -$ _____ $= 2$	$6 +$ _____ $= 11$
$15 - 9 =$ _____	$4 +$ _____ $= 11$	$19 -$ _____ $= 12$

4. Add in columns.

   a. $\$0.39 + \$0.55$ **b.** $\$2.25 + \$0.89$ **c.** $\$5.53 + \$2.69$

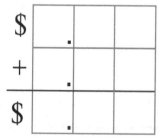   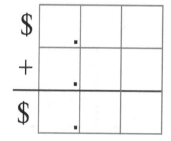   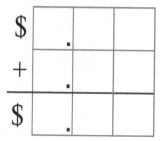

71

5. **a.** How many corners does the shape have? _____

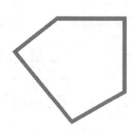

 b. What is the shape called? _____

6. In a game, Amy has 15 marbles and John has 5 fewer marbles than Amy. How many does John have?

 How many marbles do Amy and John have together?

7. Jeremy ate 4 slices of pie, which was two fewer pieces than what Eva ate. How many did Eva eat?

8. Add and subtract mentally.

a.	b.	c.
507 + 30 = _____	640 − 40 = _____	552 − 20 = _____
507 + 300 = _____	640 − 400 = _____	552 − 200 = _____

9. Subtract. Check by adding!

a.	Check:	**b.**	Check:
6 7 0 − 3 3 8	+ _____	5 4 1 − 2 7 1	+ _____

10. Count up to find the change. You can draw in the coins to help you.

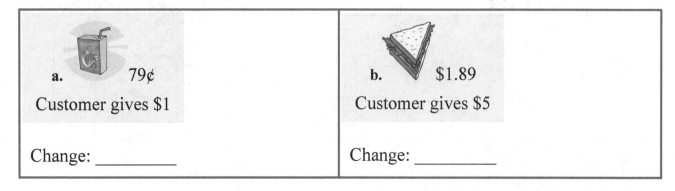

a.   79¢

Customer gives $1

Change: _____

b. $1.89

Customer gives $5

Change: _____

Cumulative Review, Grade 2, Chapters 1 - 10

1. Color in the chart all the even numbers.

1	2	3	4	5	6	7	8	9	10
11	12	13	14	15	16	17	18	19	20
21	22	23	24	25	26	27	28	29	30

2. **a.** Today is January 5. I am going away for three weeks and two days. What day will I return? (See the calendar on the right.)

January

Su	Mo	Tu	We	Th	Fr	Sa
		1	2	3	4	5
6	7	8	9	10	11	12
13	14	15	16	17	18	19
20	21	22	23	24	25	26
27	28	29	30	31		

b. I went to the gym every Wednesday in January. What were the dates I went to the gym?

3. Aunt Cindy gave Aiden and Samantha $30. The children shared the money equally. Samantha already had $5 in her piggy bank. How much money does Samantha have now?

4. Subtract.

a. $975 - 246$

b. $629 - 189$

c. $514 - 323$

d. $650 - 126$

5. Find the missing numbers.

a. $900 + \boxed{} = 914$	b. $620 + \boxed{} = 680$	c. $600 - \boxed{} = 570$
d. $\boxed{} - 20 = 40$	e. $\boxed{} - 70 = 70$	f. $572 - \boxed{} = 512$

6. Write the amounts using the dollar symbol and a decimal point.

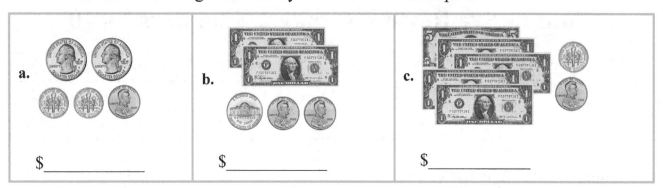

a.	b.	c.
$_____	$_____	$_____

7. Fay bought apples for $1.48 and gave the clerk $5.00.
   What was her change?

8. What is the total if you have six dimes,
   three nickels and a quarter?

9. Weigh yourself. I weigh _____. Now weigh yourself holding as many

   books as you can hold. I weigh _____ with the books.

   How much do the books weigh? _____

10. Solve.

a. Mia has saved $28. She wants to buy a sewing kit for $45. After she earns $13, can she buy it?	b. Find the cost of buying three rakes for $17 each.	c. One sack of potatoes weighs 22 kg. How much do four sacks weigh?
+	+	+

74